W9-APJ-184

What Can I Buy?

by Julie Moriarty
illustrated by Joe Cepeda

Text copyright © 2004 by Scholastic Inc.
Illustrations copyright © 2004 by Joe Cepeda.
All rights reserved. Published by Scholastic Inc.
Printed in the U.S.A.

ISBN 0-439-69712-3

SCHOLASTIC and associated logos and designs are trademarks and/or registered trademarks of Scholastic Inc.

7 8 9 10   40   12 11 10 09

SCHOLASTIC INC.
New York Toronto London Auckland Sydney
Mexico City New Delhi Hong Kong Buenos Aires

I'm going to the mall.

I want to buy school supplies.

I have four dollars.
What can I buy?

PENCILS
$1.00

Pencils
$1.00

Notebooks
$3.00

Crayons
$4.00

4

Crayons cost four dollars.

I have four dollars.

I can buy a box of crayons.

Let's color!

It's Mom's birthday.

I'm going to the mall.

I want to buy Mom a gift.

I have two dollars.
What can I buy?

Cards
$2.00

Hairbrush
$4.00

Clock
$15.00

8

A card costs two dollars.

I have two dollars.

I can buy a card.

Happy Birthday, Mom!

We're going to the movies.
I want a snack.

I have five dollars.
What can I buy?

Popcorn costs two dollars.

I have five dollars.

I can buy some popcorn!

One small popcorn, please.

Yum, yum!

We're going to the pet store.
I want to get a pet.

I have five dollars.
What can I buy?

Kitten
$20.00

Goldfish
$5.00

Puppy
$50.00

A goldfish costs five dollars.

I have five dollars.

Can I buy a goldfish?

Yes, I can buy a goldfish!

I love you, Goldie!